Contents

Introduction

About this book

1   This Approved Code of Practice (ACOP) gives advice on the requirements of the Health and Safety at Work etc Act 1974 (the HSW Act)[1] and the Control of Substances Hazardous to Health Regulations 2002 (COSHH)[2] and applies to the risk from exposure to legionella bacteria (the causative agent of legionellosis, including Legionnaires' disease). In particular it gives guidance on sections 2, 3, 4 and 6 of the HSW Act and regulations 6, 7, 8, 9 and 12 of COSHH. The Code also gives guidance on compliance with the relevant parts of the Management of Health and Safety at Work Regulations 1999 (the Management Regulations).[3]

2   This book is for dutyholders, which includes employers and those with responsibilities for the control of premises, eg landlords. To comply with their legal duties, dutyholders should:

(a)   identify and assess sources of risk. This includes checking whether conditions will encourage bacteria to multiply. For example, if the water temperature is between 20–45 °C, if there is a means of creating and disseminating breathable droplets, such as the aerosol created, eg by cooling towers, showers and spa pools; and if there are 'at risk' susceptible people who may be exposed to the contaminated aerosols (see paragraphs 28–47);
(b)   if appropriate, prepare a written scheme for preventing or controlling the risk (see paragraphs 58–64);
(c)   implement, manage and monitor precautions – if control measures are to remain effective, regular monitoring of the systems and control measures is essential (see paragraphs 65–69). Monitoring general bacterial numbers can indicate whether you are achieving microbiological control and sampling for legionella is another means of checking that a system is under control (see paragraph 68);
(d)   keep records of the precautions (see paragraphs 70–74);
(e)   appoint a competent person with sufficient authority and knowledge of the installation to help take the measures needed to comply with the law (see paragraphs 48–51).

3   The Code and guidance also set out the responsibilities of suppliers of services such as water treatment and maintenance; and designers, manufacturers, importers, suppliers and installers of systems (see paragraphs 75–85).

4   This fourth edition of the ACOP and guidance on regulations contains revisions to simplify and clarify the text. The main changes are:

(a)   removing Part 2, the technical guidance, which is now published separately at www.hse.gov.uk/pubns/books/hsg274.htm and has three parts: *Part 1: Evaporative cooling systems; Part 2: Hot and cold water systems* and *Part 3: Other risk systems*;
(b)   guidance on the following issues now has ACOP status:

(i)   risk assessment;

(ii)   the specific role of the appointed competent person, known as the 'responsible person';

(iii)   the control scheme and what it should include;

(iv)   review of control measures;

(v)   duties and responsibilities of those involved in the supply of water systems including suppliers of services, designers, manufacturers, importers, suppliers and installers of water systems.

About ACOPs

5   ACOPs are approved by the HSE Board with the consent of the Secretary of State (see 'Appendix 1: Notice of Approval' for details).

6   The ACOP describes preferred or recommended methods that can be used (or standards to be met) to comply with the Regulations and the duties imposed by the Health and Safety at Work etc Act 1974. The guidance also provides advice on achieving compliance, or it may give general information, including explaining the requirements of the law, more specific technical information or references to further sources of information.

7   The legal status of the ACOP and guidance text is clearly outlined on page 2.

Presentation

8   The ACOP text is set out in **bold**, and guidance is in normal type and the reference to the regulation(s) is in *italics*. Coloured borders indicate each section clearly.

9   Each regulation reference is followed by a short summary of the main duties imposed by that regulation and aims to help the reader navigate the document. This text is for information and does not have ACOP or guidance status.

Legionnaires' disease

10   Legionellosis is a collective term for diseases caused by legionella bacteria including the most serious legionnaires' disease, as well as the similar but less serious conditions of Pontiac fever and Lochgoilhead fever. Legionnaires' disease is a potentially fatal form of pneumonia and everyone is susceptible to infection. The risk increases with age, but some people are at higher risk, eg people over 45, smokers and heavy drinkers, people suffering from chronic respiratory or kidney disease, diabetes, lung and heart disease or anyone with an impaired immune system.

11   The bacterium *Legionella pneumophila* and related bacteria are common in natural water sources such as rivers, lakes and reservoirs, but usually in low numbers. They may also be found in purpose-built water systems, such as cooling towers, evaporative condensers, hot and cold water systems and spa pools. If conditions are favourable, the bacteria may multiply, increasing the risks of legionnaires' disease, and it is therefore important to control the risks by introducing appropriate measures.

12   Legionella bacteria are widespread in natural water systems, eg rivers and ponds. However, the conditions are rarely conducive for people to catch the disease from these sources. Outbreaks of the illness occur from exposure to legionella growing in purpose-built systems where water is maintained at a temperature high enough to encourage growth, eg cooling towers, evaporative

condensers, hot and cold water systems and spa pools used in all sorts of premises (work and domestic).

13 Legionnaires' disease is normally contracted by inhaling small droplets of water (aerosols), suspended in the air, containing the bacteria. Certain conditions increase the risk from legionella if:

(a) the water temperature in all or some parts of the system may be between 20–45 °C, which is suitable for growth;
(b) it is possible for water droplets to be produced and if so, they can be dispersed;
(c) water is stored and/or re-circulated;
(d) there are deposits that can support bacterial growth, such as rust, sludge, scale, organic matter and biofilms.

14 It is important to control the risks by introducing measures which do not allow proliferation of the organisms in the water systems and reduce, so far as is reasonably practicable, exposure to water droplets and aerosol. This will reduce the possibility of creating conditions in which the risk from exposure to legionella bacteria is increased.

Health and safety law

15 Duties under the HSW Act apply to the risks from exposure to legionella bacteria that may arise from work activities. The Management Regulations provide a broad framework for controlling health and safety at work. As well as requiring risk assessments, they also require employers to have access to competent help in applying the provisions of health and safety law; to establish procedures for workers if there are situations presenting serious, imminent danger; and for co-operation and co-ordination where two or more employers or self-employed people share a workplace. More specifically, COSHH provides a framework of actions designed to control the risk from a range of hazardous substances, including biological agents.

Information box: Summary of the HSW Act, sections 2, 3 and 4

Section 2 places a duty on employers to ensure the health, safety and welfare of employees so far as reasonably practicable (SFARP). More guidance on the principles of SFARP may be found on the HSE website (www.hse.gov.uk/risk/theory/alarp1.htm). Section 2 also requires employers to consult with trade union safety representatives on matters affecting health and safety in the workplace. Employers of more than five people must also prepare a written health and safety policy and bring it to the attention of employees.

Section 3 requires employers to ensure that non-employees who may be affected by work activities are not exposed to risks to their health and safety.

Section 4 places a duty on anyone responsible for the workplace to ensure that the premises, plant and machinery do not endanger the people using them.

---

16 Only the courts can give an authoritative interpretation of law on the application of these Regulations and guidance to people working under another's direction. If people working under the control and direction of others are treated as self-employed for tax and national insurance purposes, they may nevertheless be treated as employees for health and safety purposes. So, it may be necessary to take appropriate action to protect them. If there is any doubt about who is

responsible for the health and safety of a worker, clarify this and include it in the terms of a contract. However, a legal duty under section 3 of the HSW Act cannot be passed on by means of a contract. You will still have duties towards others under section 3 of the HSW Act. If you employ workers on the understanding that they are responsible for their own health and safety, seek legal advice before doing so. For section 3 to apply:

(a)   there must be a dutyholder – either an employer or a self-employed person; and

(b)   there must be a risk to the health or safety of a person who is not an employee of the dutyholder or the self-employed dutyholder themselves; and

(c)   that risk must arise from the conduct of the dutyholder's undertaking. 'Undertaking' means 'enterprise' or 'business'.

Section 3 does not apply to:

(d)   welfare issues (such as the provision of toilets or washing facilities);

(e)   nuisance or amenity issues that have no health or safety implications (such as unpleasant smells arising from work activities);

(f)   poor workmanship, where trading standards or contractual remedies may exist, unless they have demonstrably compromised health and safety.

17   COSHH provides a framework of actions designed to control the risk from a range of hazardous substances, including biological agents. The essential elements of COSHH are:

(a)   risk assessment;

(b)   where reasonably practicable, prevention of exposure or substitution with a less hazardous substance, or substitution of a process or method with a less hazardous one;

(c)   control of exposure, where prevention or substitution is not reasonably practicable;

(d)   maintenance, examination and testing of control measures;

(e)   provision of information, instruction and training for employees;

(f)   health surveillance of employees (where appropriate, and if there are valid techniques for detecting indications of disease) where exposure may result in an identifiable disease or adverse health effect.

18   The Reporting of Injuries, Diseases and Dangerous Occurrences Regulations 2013 (RIDDOR)[4] require employers and others, eg someone who has control of work premises, to report to HSE, accidents and some diseases that arise out of or in connection with work. Cases of legionellosis are reportable under RIDDOR if:

(a)   a doctor notifies the employer; and

(b)   the employee's current job involves work on or near cooling systems which are located in the workplace and use water; or work on water service systems located in the workplace which are likely to be a source of contamination.

For more guidance on RIDDOR, see www.hse.gov.uk/riddor/index.htm.

19   Those who have, to any extent, control of premises, have a duty under the Notification of Cooling Towers and Evaporative Condensers Regulations 1992[5] to notify the local authority in writing with details of 'notifiable devices'. These are cooling towers and evaporative condensers, except when they contain water that is not exposed to the air and the water and electricity supply are not connected. If a tower becomes redundant and decommissioned or dismantled, it should also be notified. Although the requirement is to notify the local authority, the relevant

authority (ie HSE or the local authority) for the premises concerned enforces the Regulations. Notification forms are available from the local authority or local environmental health department. The main purpose of these Regulations is to help investigate outbreaks.

20   The Safety Representatives and Safety Committees Regulations 1977 and the Health and Safety (Consultation with Employees) Regulations 1996[6] require employers to consult trade union safety representatives, other employee representatives, or employees where there are no representatives, about health and safety matters. This includes changes to work that may affect their health and safety at work, arrangements for getting competent help, information on the risks and controls, and planning of health and safety training.

21   You can find more information in the HSE leaflet *Legionnaires' disease: A brief guide for dutyholders*[7] and at www.hse.gov.uk/legionnaires/index.htm.

Scope and application

22   This Approved Code of Practice applies to the control of legionella bacteria, in any undertaking involving a work activity managed by you or on your behalf. It applies to premises controlled in connection with a trade, business or other undertaking where water is used or stored; and where there is a means of creating and transmitting water droplets (aerosols) which may be inhaled, causing a reasonably foreseeable risk of exposure to legionella bacteria.

23   There is a reasonably foreseeable risk of exposure to legionella bacteria in:

(a)   cooling systems with cooling towers, evaporative condensers or dry/wet cooling systems;
(b)   hot and cold water systems;
(c)   spa pools (see paragraph 24);
(d)   other plant and systems containing water that can create and increase the risk from legionella during operation or when being maintained (see paragraphs 13, 14 and 27).

24   These systems present a risk of exposure to legionella bacteria. There is further technical guidance on these systems in *Part 1: Evaporative cooling systems*; *Part 2: Hot and cold water systems* and *Part 3: Other risk systems* at www.hse.gov.uk/pubns/books/hsg274.htm. Specific guidance on managing spa pools is available at www.hse.gov.uk/legionnaires/spa-pools.htm.

25   All systems require a risk assessment, however not all systems will require elaborate control measures. A simple risk assessment may show that the risks are low and being properly managed to comply with the law. In such cases, you may not need to take further action, but it is important to review your assessment regularly in case of any changes in your system, and specifically if there is reason to suspect it is no longer valid. There is more information specifically for those in control of premises, eg landlords, in *Part 2: Hot and cold water systems* at www.hse.gov.uk/pubns/books/hsg274.htm and at www.hse.gov.uk/legionnaires/what-you-must-do.htm.

Information box

An example of a low risk situation may be found:

(a)   in a small building without individuals especially 'at risk' from legionella bacteria;
(b)   where daily water usage is inevitable and sufficient to turn over the entire system;
(c)   where cold water is directly from a wholesome mains supply (no stored water tanks);
(d)   where hot water is fed from instantaneous heaters or low volume water heaters (supplying outlets at 50 °C);
(e)   where the only outlets are toilets and wash hand basins (no showers).

Guidance

26   A water system includes all plant/equipment and components associated with that system, eg all associated pipework, pumps, feed tanks, valves, showers, heat exchangers, quench tanks, water softeners, chillers etc. It is important to consider the system as a whole and not, eg the cooling tower in isolation. Deadlegs and parts of the system used intermittently, eg test loops in engineering factories and injection moulding machines, also need to be included as part of the system, because they can create particular problems with microbial growth going unnoticed. Once brought back online they can cause heavy contamination, which could disrupt the efficacy of the water treatment regime.

27   For other risk systems, such as humidifiers and air washers, vehicle washes, wet scrubbers, indoor fountains and water features, see the advice on control measures in *Part 3: Other risk systems* at www.hse.gov.uk/pubns/books/hsg274.htm.

Identification and assessment of the risk

Regulation

COSHH, regulation 6; Management Regulations, regulation 3; HSW Act, sections 2, 3 and 4.

Summary

These Regulations require employers to make a suitable and sufficient assessment of the risks from any work liable to expose employees to any substance hazardous to health, before that work is carried out. Employers are also required to make an assessment of the risks to other people not in their employment who may be affected by the work activity. They are also required to regularly review the risk assessment, and make any necessary changes as a result of the review.

ACOP

28   A suitable and sufficient assessment must be carried out to identify and assess the risk of exposure to legionella bacteria from work activities and water systems on the premises and any precautionary measures needed. The dutyholder is responsible for ensuring the risk assessment is carried out. The dutyholder is either:

(a)   the employer, where the risk from their undertaking is to their employees or others; or
(b)   a self-employed person, where there is a risk from their undertaking to themselves or others; or
(c)   the person who is in control of premises or systems in connection with work, where there is a risk from systems in the building, eg where a building is let to tenants, but the landlord keeps responsibility for its maintenance.

29   The dutyholder must ensure that the person who carries out the risk assessment and provides advice on prevention and control of exposure must be competent to do so.

30   The risk assessment should identify and evaluate potential sources of risk and:

(a)   the particular means of preventing exposure to legionella bacteria; or
(b)   if prevention is not reasonably practicable, the particular means of controlling the risk from exposure to legionella bacteria.

31 Where the assessment demonstrates there is no reasonably foreseeable risk or that risks are insignificant and unlikely to increase, and are properly managed, no further assessment or measures are needed. However, if the situation changes, the assessment should be reviewed and revised, if any changes are needed.

32 You need to review the assessment regularly and specifically when there is reason to believe that the original risk assessment may no longer be valid. You should also review management and communication procedures as appropriate.

33 Before any formal health and safety management system for water systems is implemented, the dutyholder should carry out a risk assessment to identify the possible risks. The purpose of the assessment is to enable a decision on:

(a) the risk to health, ie whether the potential for harm to health from exposure is reasonably foreseeable, unless adequate precautionary measures are taken;

(b) the necessary measures to prevent, or adequately control, the risk from exposure to legionella bacteria.

34 The risk assessment also enables the dutyholder to show they have considered all the relevant factors, and the steps needed to prevent or control the risk.

35 The dutyholder may need access to competent help and advice when carrying out the risk assessment. For further guidance on this, see paragraphs 48–51. This source of advice may not necessarily be from within the person's organisation but may be from a consultancy, water treatment company or a person experienced in carrying out risk assessments. Employers are required to consult employees or their representatives about the arrangements for getting competent help and advice (see paragraph 20).

36 The dutyholder under paragraph 28 should, with the help of the appointed responsible person, make reasonable enquiries to ensure that organisations such as water treatment companies or consultants, and staff from the occupier's organisation, are competent and suitably trained and have the necessary equipment to carry out their duties in the written scheme safely and adequately.

37 Few workplaces stay the same, so it makes sense to review regularly what you are doing. Further guidance on risk assessment is at www.hse.gov.uk/risk.

Carrying out a risk assessment

38 As part of the risk assessment, take into account the individual nature of each site and consider the system as a whole and not, eg the cooling tower in isolation. In complex systems, a site survey of all the water systems should be carried out, including an asset register of all associated plant, pumps, strainers and other relevant items. This should include an up-to-date schematic diagram showing the layout of the plant or system, including parts temporarily out of use.

39 Consider the individual nature of the site and system as a whole, including deadlegs and parts of the system used intermittently. These should be included because they can create particular problems, as microbial growth can go unnoticed. When they are brought back online, they can cause heavy contamination, which could disrupt the efficacy of the water treatment regime.

Guidance

40   A schematic diagram is an important tool to show the layout of the plant or system, including parts temporarily out of use and should be made available to inform the risk assessment process. These are not formal technical drawings and are intended to be easy to read without specialised training or experience. While providing only an indication of the size and scale, they allow someone unfamiliar with the layout of a system to understand the relative positions and connections of the relevant components quickly. They also help the person who carries out the assessment in paragraphs 28–29 decide which parts of the water system, eg which specific equipment and services, may pose a risk to those at work or other people.

41   There are a number of factors that create a risk of someone acquiring legionellosis, such as:

(a)   the presence of legionella bacteria;
(b)   conditions suitable for growth of the organisms, eg suitable water temperature (20 °C–45 °C) and deposits that are a source of nutrients for the organism, such as sludge, scale, rust, algae, other organic matter and biofilms;
(c)   a means of creating and spreading breathable droplets, eg the aerosol generated by cooling towers, showers or spa pools;
(d)   the presence (and numbers) of people who may be exposed, especially in premises where occupants are particularly vulnerable, eg healthcare, residential and nursing homes.

42   The following list contains some of the factors to consider, as appropriate, when carrying out the risk assessment:

(a)   the source of system supply water, eg whether from a mains supply or not;
(b)   possible sources of contamination of the supply water in the premises before it reaches the cold water storage tank, calorifier, cooling tower or any other system using water that may present a risk of exposure to legionella bacteria;
(c)   the normal plant operating characteristics;
(d)   unusual, but reasonably foreseeable operating conditions, eg breakdowns;
(e)   any means of disinfection in use;
(f)   the review of any current control measures;
(g)   the local environment.

43   Where there are five or more employees, the significant findings of the assessment must be recorded (see paragraphs 70–74) but in any case, it may be necessary to record sufficient details of the assessment to be able to show that it has been done. Link the record of the assessment to other relevant health and safety records and, in particular, the written scheme referred to in paragraphs 58–64.

44   Employers must consult employees or their representatives on the identified risks of exposure to legionella bacteria and the measures and actions taken to control the risks (see paragraph 20). Employees should be given an opportunity to comment on the assessment and control measures and the employer should take account of these views, so it is important for employers to publicise to employees that a legionella risk assessment has been performed. Employers may wish to involve employees and/or safety representatives when carrying out and reviewing risk assessments as a good way of helping to manage health and safety risk.

45   It is essential to monitor the effectiveness of the control measures and make decisions about when and how monitoring should take place.

46   If the risks are considered insignificant and are being properly managed to comply with the law, the assessment is complete. It may not be necessary to take

Guidance

any further action, but it is important to review the assessment periodically, in case anything has changed.

47   The record of the assessment is a living document that must be reviewed to ensure it remains up-to-date. Arrange to review the assessment regularly and specifically whenever there is reason to suspect it is no longer valid. An indication of when to review the assessment and what to consider should be recorded. This may result from, eg:

(a)   changes to the water system or its use;
(b)   changes to the use of the building in which the water system is installed;
(c)   the availability of new information about risks or control measures;
(d)   the results of checks indicating that control measures are no longer effective;
(e)   changes to key personnel;
(f)   a case of legionnaires' disease/legionellosis associated with the system.

Managing the risk: Management responsibilities, training and competence

Regulation

COSHH, regulations 8 and 12; Management Regulations, regulations 5, 7, 10 and 13; HSW Act, sections 2, 3 and 4.

Summary

These Regulations require employers to take reasonable steps to ensure that any control measures are properly used and applied. They require employees to make full and proper use of those control measures. Employers are also required to have arrangements in place for the management of health and safety, to have access to competent health and safety advice and to provide employees with suitable and sufficient information, instruction, and training.

ACOP

48   If the assessment shows that there is a reasonably foreseeable risk and it is reasonably practicable to prevent exposure or control the risk from exposure, the dutyholder under paragraph 28 should appoint a competent person or persons to help undertake the measures needed to comply with the requirements in COSHH. The appointed competent person or persons should have sufficient authority, competence and knowledge of the installation to ensure that all operational procedures are carried out in a timely and effective manner. Where the dutyholder does not employ anyone with the necessary competence, they may need to appoint people from outside the organisation. In such circumstances, the dutyholder should take all reasonable steps to ensure the competence of those carrying out work who are not under their direct control and that responsibilities and lines of communication are properly established and clearly laid down.

49   Those appointed under paragraph 48 to carry out the risk assessment and draw up and implement precautionary measures should have such ability, experience, instruction, information, training and resources to enable them to carry out their tasks competently and safely. In particular, they should know the:

(a)   potential sources of legionella bacteria and the risks they present;
(b)   measures to adopt, including the precautions to take to protect the people concerned, and their significance;

ACOP

Guidance

(c) **measures to take to ensure that the control measures remain effective, and their significance.**

50   Inadequate management, lack of training and poor communication are all contributory factors in outbreaks of legionnaires' disease. It is therefore important that the people involved in assessing risk and applying precautions are competent, trained and aware of their responsibilities.

51   The dutyholder should specifically appoint a competent person or persons to take day-to-day responsibility for controlling any identified risk from legionella bacteria, known as the 'responsible person'. It is important for the appointed responsible person to have *sufficient authority, competence and knowledge of the installation* to ensure that all operational procedures are carried out effectively and in a timely way. Those specifically appointed to implement the control measures and strategies should be suitably informed, instructed and trained and their suitability assessed. They must be properly trained to a level that ensures tasks are carried out in a safe, technically competent manner; and receive regular refresher training. Keep records of all initial and refresher training. If a dutyholder is self-employed or a member of a partnership, and is competent, they may appoint themselves. The appointed responsible person should have a clear understanding of their role and the overall health and safety management structure and policy in the organisation. See *Managing for health and safety at work* for further guidance.[8]

Competence

52   The dutyholder should also ensure that all employees involved in work that may expose an employee or other person to legionella are given suitable and sufficient information, instruction and training. This includes information, instruction and training on the significant findings of the risk assessment and the appropriate precautions and actions they need to take to safeguard themselves and others. This should be reviewed and updated whenever significant changes are made to the type of work carried out or methods used. Training is an essential element of an employee's capability to carry out work safely, but it is not the only factor: instructions, experience, knowledge and other personal qualities are also relevant to perform a task safely.

Implementation of the control scheme

53   Monitor the implementation of the written scheme (detailed in paragraphs 58–64) for the prevention and control of the risk. Supervise everyone involved in any related operational procedure properly. Define staff responsibilities and lines of communication properly and document them clearly.

54   Make arrangements to ensure that appropriate staff levels are available during all hours the water system is operating. The precise requirements will depend on the nature and complexity of the water system. In some cases, eg where there is complex cooling plant, shift working and arrangements to cover for all absences from duty, for whatever reason, may be necessary. Appropriate arrangements should be made to ensure that the responsible person, or an authorised deputy, can be contacted at all times.

55   Also, make call-out arrangements for people engaged in the management of water systems which operate automatically. Details of the contact arrangements for emergency call-out personnel should be clearly displayed at access points to all automatically or remotely controlled water systems.

56 Communications and management procedures are particularly important where several people are responsible for different aspects of the operational procedures. For example, responsibility for applying control measures may change when shift work is involved, or when the person who monitors the efficacy of a water treatment regime may not be the person who applies it. In such circumstances, responsibilities should be well defined in writing and understood by all concerned. Lines of communication should be clear, unambiguous and audited regularly to ensure they are effective. This also applies to outside companies and consultants who may be responsible for certain parts of the control regime.

57 Employing contractors or consultants does not absolve the dutyholder of responsibility for ensuring that control procedures are carried out to the standard required to prevent the proliferation of legionella bacteria. Dutyholders should make reasonable enquiries to satisfy themselves of the competence of contractors in the area of work before they enter into contracts for the treatment, monitoring, and cleaning of the water system, and other aspects of water treatment and control. An illustration of the levels of service to expect from Service Providers can be found in the Code of Conduct administered by the Legionella Control Association (LCA).[9]

Preventing or controlling the risk from exposure to legionella bacteria

Regulation

COSHH, regulations 7 and 9; HSW Act, sections 2, 3 and 4.

Summary

These Regulations require employers to prevent, or where this is not reasonably practicable, adequately control, the exposure of any employees to substances hazardous to health. Employers are also required to maintain, examine and test control measures and, at suitable intervals review and, if necessary, revise those measures. They must also keep suitable records of examinations, tests and repairs of control measures.

ACOP

58 Where the assessment shows that there is a reasonably foreseeable risk of exposure to legionella bacteria, the use of water systems, parts of water systems or systems of work that lead to exposure must be avoided so far as is reasonably practicable. Where this is not reasonably practicable, there should be a written scheme for controlling the risk from exposure that should be properly implemented and managed. The written scheme should specify measures to take to ensure that it remains effective.

59 The risk from exposure should normally be controlled by measures which do not allow the growth of legionella bacteria in the system and which reduce exposure to water droplets and aerosols. Precautions should, where appropriate, include the following:

(a) **avoiding water temperatures between 20 °C and 45 °C and conditions that favour the growth of legionella bacteria and other microorganisms;**

(b) **avoiding water stagnation which may encourage the growth of biofilm;**

(c) **avoiding the use of materials that harbour bacteria and other microorganisms, or provide nutrients for microbial growth. The *Water Fittings and Materials Directory*[10] references fittings, materials, and appliances approved for their compliance with the UK legal requirements for plumbing fittings and water using appliances;**

ACOP

(d) controlling the release of water spray;
(e) maintaining the cleanliness of the system and water in it;
(f) using water treatment techniques;
(g) taking action to ensure the correct and safe operation and maintenance of the water system.

60 The written scheme should include, where appropriate, and with reference to the risk assessment:

(a) an up-to-date plan showing the layout of the plant or water system, including parts temporarily out of use (a schematic diagram is sufficient);
(b) a description of the correct and safe operation of the system;
(c) the precautions to take;
(d) checks to carry out to ensure the written scheme is effective and the frequency of such checks;
(e) the remedial action to take if the written scheme is shown to be not effective.

Guidance

61 Once the risk has been identified and assessed, a written scheme should be prepared for preventing or controlling it. In particular, the written scheme should contain the information about the water system needed to control the risk from exposure. However, if it is decided that the risks are insignificant and are being properly managed to comply with the law, you may not need to take any further action. But it is important to review the risk assessment regularly and specifically if there is reason to suspect it is no longer valid, for example changes in the water system or its use. The primary objective should be to avoid conditions that allow legionella bacteria to proliferate and to avoid creating a spray or aerosol. It may be possible to prevent the risk of exposure by, eg, using dry cooling plant. Where this is not reasonably practicable, the risk may be controlled by minimising the release of droplets and ensuring water conditions that prevent the proliferation of legionella bacteria. This might include engineering controls, cleaning protocols and other control strategies. Make decisions about the maintenance procedures and intervals, where relevant, on equipment used for implementing the control measures. Legionella bacteria may be present in low or very low numbers in many water systems, but careful control will prevent them from multiplying.

62 The written scheme should give details on how to use and carry out the various control measures and water treatment regimes, including:

(a) the physical treatment programme – eg using temperature control for hot and cold water systems;
(b) the chemical treatment programme, including a description of the manufacturer's data on effectiveness, the concentrations and contact time required;
(c) health and safety information for storage, handling, use and disposal of chemicals;
(d) system control parameters (together with allowable tolerances); physical, chemical and biological parameters, together with measurement methods and sampling locations, test frequencies and procedures for maintaining consistency;
(e) remedial measures to take in case the control limits are exceeded, including lines of communication;
(f) cleaning and disinfection procedures;
(g) emergency procedures.

63 The written scheme should also describe the correct operation of the water system plant, including:

Guidance

(a)   commissioning and recommissioning procedures;
(b)   shutdown procedures;
(c)   checks of warning systems and diagnostic systems in case of system malfunctions;
(d)   maintenance requirements and frequencies;
(e)   operating cycles – including when the system plant is in use or idle.

64   See www.hse.gov.uk/pubns/books/hsg274.htm for detailed guidance on how to effectively prevent or control exposure.

ACOP

Review of control measures: Monitoring and routine inspection

65   For precautions to remain effective, the condition and performance of the system will need to be monitored. The appointed responsible person should oversee and manage this. Or, where appropriate, an external contractor or an independent third party can do it. Management should involve:

(a)   checking the performance and operation of the system and its component parts;
(b)   inspecting the accessible parts of the system for damage and signs of contamination;
(c)   monitoring to ensure that the treatment regime continues to control to the required standard.

Guidance

66   The frequency and extent of routine monitoring will depend on the operating characteristics of the water system.

67   Testing of water quality is an essential part of the treatment regime, particularly in cooling systems. It may be carried out by a service provider, such as a water treatment company or consultant, or by the operator, provided they have been trained to do so and are properly supervised. The type of tests required will depend on the nature of the water system. Further details are given at www.hse.gov.uk/pubns/books/hsg274.htm for both cooling systems and hot and cold water systems.

68   The routine monitoring of general bacterial numbers (total viable count) is also appropriate as an indication of whether microbiological control is being achieved. This is generally only carried out for cooling tower systems, but it is also recommended for spa pools (see www.hse.gov.uk/legionnaires/spa-pools.htm for further guidance). The risk assessment will help identify if you need to conduct routine monitoring in the specific system. Periodic sampling and testing for the presence of legionella bacteria may also be relevant to show that adequate control is being achieved. However, reliably detecting the presence of legionella bacteria is technically difficult and requires specialist laboratory facilities. The interpretation of results is also difficult; a negative result is no guarantee that legionella bacteria are not present in the system. Conversely, a positive result may not indicate a failure of controls, as legionella are present in almost all natural water sources. Further guidance on bacteriological monitoring and interpretation of test results is at www.hse.gov.uk/pubns/books/hsg274.htm.

69   A suitably experienced and competent person should interpret the results of monitoring and testing. Carry out any remedial measures promptly, where needed.

Record keeping

Regulation

COSHH, regulations 6 and 9; Management Regulations, regulations 3 and 5; HSW Act, sections 2, 3 and 4.

> ## Summary
>
> These Regulations require employers, where they have five or more employees, to record the significant findings of their risk assessment and the steps taken to prevent exposure to substances hazardous to health. Employers are also required to keep suitable records of examinations, tests and repairs of control measures.

ACOP

70   An assessment of the risk must be carried out and those appointed under paragraph 48 must record the significant findings and ensure appropriate records are kept. This should include any groups of employees identified as being particularly at risk and the steps taken to prevent or control risks. If the employer has less than five employees there is no statutory duty to write anything down, but it may be useful to keep a written record of what has been done.

71   Records should include details about:

(a)   the appointed responsible person(s) for conducting the risk assessment, managing, and implementing the written scheme;
(b)   any significant findings of the risk assessment;
(c)   the written scheme and its implementation;
(d)   details about the state of operation of the water system, ie in use/not in use;
(e)   the results of any monitoring inspection, test or check carried out, and the dates.

72   These records should be retained throughout the period they are current and for at least two years afterwards. Retain records of any monitoring inspection, test or check carried out, and the dates, for at least five years.

Guidance

73   To ensure that precautions continue to be applied and that adequate information is available, where there are five employees or more, you must keep a record of the assessment, the precautionary measures, and the treatments. All records should be signed, verified or authenticated by those people performing the various tasks assigned to them.

74   The following items should normally be recorded:

(a)   names and positions of people responsible, and their deputies, for carrying out the various tasks under the written scheme;
(b)   a risk assessment and a written scheme of actions and control measures;
(c)   schematic diagrams of the water systems;
(d)   details of precautionary measures that have been applied/implemented including enough detail to show that they were applied/implemented correctly, and the dates on which they were carried out;
(e)   remedial work required and carried out, and the date of completion;
(f)   a log detailing visits by contractors, consultants and other personnel;
(g)   cleaning and disinfection procedures and associated reports and certificates;
(h)   results of the chemical analysis of the water;
(i)   results of any biological monitoring;

Guidance

(j)   information on other hazards, eg treatment chemicals;
(k)   cooling tower and evaporative condenser notification;
(l)   training records of personnel;
(m) the name and position of the person or people who have responsibilities for implementing the written scheme, their respective responsibilities and their lines of communication;
(n)   records showing the current state of operation of the water system, eg when the system or plant is in use and, if not in use, whether it is drained down;
(o)   either the signature of the person carrying out the work, or other form of authentication where appropriate.

Responsibilities of designers, manufacturers, importers, suppliers and installers

Regulation

HSW Act, sections 3 and 6.

Summary

This places a duty on any person who designs, manufactures, imports or supplies articles or substances for use at work, to ensure that they are safe and without risks to health at work and that any information related to the article or substance is provided.

ACOP

75   Designers, manufacturers, importers, suppliers and installers of water systems that may create a risk of exposure to legionella bacteria, must:

(a)   **ensure, so far as is reasonably practicable, that the water system is so designed and constructed that it will be safe and without risks to health when used at work;**
(b)   **provide adequate information for the user about the risk and measures necessary to ensure that the water systems will be safe and without risks to health when used at work. This should be updated in the light of any new information about significant risks to health and safety that becomes available, so that dutyholders can ensure relevant changes are made to their risk assessment and controls.**

Regulation

HSW Act, sections 3 and 6.

Summary

This places general duties on employers and the self-employed to conduct their undertakings in such a way as to ensure, so far as is reasonably practicable, that people other than themselves or their employees are not exposed to risks to their health or safety. They should also provide adequate information regarding any aspects of their products or services that might affect their health and safety.

ACOP

76   Suppliers of products and services, including consultancy and water treatment services, aimed at preventing or controlling the risk of exposure to legionella bacteria, must, so far as is reasonably practicable ensure that:

(a)   **measures intended to control the risk of exposure to legionella bacteria are so designed and implemented that they will be effective, safe and without risks to health when used at work;**

ACOP

(b) they provide adequate information on the correct and safe use of products, taking into account the circumstances and conditions of their use;

(c) any limitations on their expertise or the products or services they offer are clearly defined and made known to the dutyholder or the appointed responsible person(s);

(d) any deficiencies or limitations which they identify in the dutyholder's systems or written scheme to control the risk of exposure to legionella bacteria are made known to the dutyholder or the appointed responsible person(s);

(e) their staff have the necessary ability, experience, instruction, information, training and resources to carry out their tasks competently and safely.

77 All water systems must be properly installed, and commissioned as appropriate.

78 Anyone involved in the supply of water systems (designers, manufacturers, importers, suppliers and installers) must, as far as is reasonably practicable, ensure that the equipment is designed and constructed so that it is safe when used at work and enable safe and easy operation, cleaning and maintenance.

79 Cooling systems should be designed and constructed so they:

(a) control the release of drift (eg by fitting effective drift eliminators that do not eliminate but rather reduce drift); and spray from other parts of the system;

(b) aid safe operation (eg water circuitry should be as simple as possible, ideally without deadlegs, or if this is not possible, limit the length of deadlegs);

(c) aid cleaning and disinfection (eg those parts of the system which need regular cleaning should be easily accessible, readily removable and easily dismantled);

(d) are made of materials which can be easily disinfected and which do not support microbial growth.

80 Hot and cold water systems should be designed and constructed so they:

(a) take account of and comply with the Water Supply (Water Fittings) Regulations 1999[11] and the Scottish Water Byelaws (see www.scottishwater.co.uk);

(b) aid safe operation (eg without deadlegs, or if this is not possible, limit the length of deadlegs limited and disconnect or remove redundant or non-essential standby plant);

(c) reduce stored cold water to the minimum needed to meet peak needs;

(d) aid cleaning and disinfection (eg by providing suitable access points in the system);

(e) minimise heat gain/loss (eg hot and cold water pipes and storage tanks should be insulated).

81 Manufacturers and suppliers of water systems must provide adequate information and instructions on their safe use. This should include information about those aspects of operation and maintenance which have a bearing on the risk.

Guidance

82   Those who supply services, such as water treatment or maintenance services should make clear to the responsible person any deficiencies in the water system or measures that may pose a significant risk of exposure to legionella bacteria. They should also make the dutyholder or the responsible person aware of any limitations in their own expertise, products or services so they can make arrangements to ensure that these deficiencies or limitations are addressed.

83   Service providers should also ensure that their staff and contractors are competent to carry out the task safely. They should be properly trained to a standard appropriate to the various tasks they perform, such as risk assessment, advising on water treatment measures, sampling or cleaning and maintaining water systems. The Legionella Control Association administers a Code of Conduct[9] for organisations providing services to occupiers/owners of water systems. This Code of Conduct does not have legal status but may give guidance to dutyholders about the standards of service they should expect to receive from service providers who abide by the Code.

84   All staff and contractors should be suitably trained, managed and supervised and given appropriate resources or support. In particular, they should be aware of the action to take in situations outside their knowledge or experience.

85   Cooling systems should also be designed and constructed so they comply with relevant British Standards or their European/International equivalents.

86   Further detailed technical guidance on how systems should be designed and constructed is available in *Part 1: Evaporative cooling systems* and *Part 2: Hot and cold water systems* at www.hse.gov.uk/pubns/books/hsg274.htm.

Appendix 1 Notice of Approval

By virtue of section 16(4) of the Health and Safety at Work etc Act 1974, and with the consent of the Secretary of State for Work and Pensions, the Health and Safety Executive has on 30 October 2013 approved the revised Code of Practice entitled *Legionnaires' disease: The control of legionella bacteria in water systems*.

The revised Code of Practice gives practical guidance with respect to sections 2, 3, 4 and 6 of the Health and Safety at Work etc Act 1974, regulations 6, 7, 8, 9 and 12 of the Control of Substances Hazardous to Health Regulations 2002 and guidance on compliance with the relevant parts of the Management of Health and Safety at Work Regulations 1999.

By virtue of section 16(5) and with the consent of the Secretary of State for Work and Pensions under that paragraph, the Health and Safety Executive has withdrawn its approval of the Code of Practice entitled *Legionnaire's disease: The control of legionella bacteria in water systems* (L8), which came into effect on 8 January 2001 which shall cease to have effect on 25 November 2013.

The Code of Practice comes into effect on 25 November 2013.

Signed

SUE JOHNS
Secretary to the Board of the Health and Safety Executive

7 November 2013

Glossary

aerosol a suspension in a gaseous medium of solid particles, liquid particles, or solid and liquid particles having negligible falling velocity. In the context of this document, it is a suspension of particles which may contain legionella with a typical droplet size of <5μm that can be inhaled deep into the lungs.

algae a small, usually aquatic, plant which requires light to grow, often found on exposed areas of **cooling towers**.

bacteria (singular bacterium) a microscopic, unicellular (or more rarely multicellular) organism.

biofilm a community of **bacteria** and other **microorganisms**, embedded in a protective layer with entrained debris, attached to a surface.

calorifier an apparatus used for the transfer of heat to water in a vessel by indirect means, the source of heat being contained within a pipe or coil immersed in the water.

cooling tower an apparatus through which warm water is discharged against an air stream; in doing so part of the water is evaporated to saturate the air and this cools the water. The cooler water is usually pumped to a heat exchanger to be reheated and recycled through the tower.

deadleg pipes leading to a fitting through which water only passes infrequently when there is draw-off from the fitting, redundant or abandoned legs of pipework.

drift circulating water lost from the tower as liquid droplets entrained in the exhaust air stream; usually expressed as a percentage of circulating water flow, but for more precise work it is parts of water per million by weight of air for a given liquid to gas ratio.

drift eliminator more correctly referred to as drift reducers or minimisers – equipment containing a complex system of baffles designed to remove water droplets from **cooling tower** air passing through it.

dry/wet cooling systems dry coolers with the capacity to employ evaporative cooling when required either due to high ambient air temperature or when cooling demand is high.

evaporative condenser a heat exchanger in which refrigerant is condensed by a combination of air movement and water sprays over its surface.

evaporative cooling a process by which a small portion of a circulating body of water is caused to evaporate, taking the required latent heat of vaporisation from the remainder of the water and cooling it.

fouling   organic growth or other deposits on heat transfer surfaces, causing loss in efficiency.

legionnaires' disease   a form of pneumonia caused by bacteria of the genus legionella.

legionella   a single bacterium of the genus **legionellae**.

legionellae   the name of a genus of bacteria which includes over 50 species and belongs to the family *Legionellaceae*. They are ubiquitous in the environment and found in a wide spectrum of natural and artificial collections of water.

Legionella pneumophila   one of the causative organisms of **legionnaires' disease**.

legionellosis   any illness caused by exposure to **legionella**.

microorganism   an organism of microscopic size including **bacteria**, fungi and viruses.

nutrient   a food source for **microorganisms**.

Pontiac fever   a disease caused by a species of legionella, an upper respiratory illness less severe than **legionnaires' disease**.

risk assessment   identifying and assessing the risk from exposure to legionella from work activities and water sources on premises and determining any necessary precautionary measures.

service provider   companies or individuals or their sub-contractors who are involved with providing advice, consultancy, operating, maintenance and management services or the supply of equipment or chemicals to the owner or occupier of premises.

sludge   a general term for soft mud-like deposits found on heat transfer surfaces or other important sections of a cooling system. Also found at the base of calorifiers and cold water storage tanks.

stagnation   the condition where water ceases to flow and is therefore liable to microbiological growth.

strainers   a coarse filter usually positioned upstream of a sensitive component such as a pump control valve or heat exchanger to protect it from debris.

References and further reading

References

1   *Health and Safety at Work etc Act 1974 (c.37)* The Stationery Office 1974
ISBN 978 0 10 543774 1

2   *Control of substances hazardous to health (COSHH). The Control of
Substances Hazardous to Health Regulations 2002 (as amended). Approved Code
of Practice and guidance* L5 (Sixth edition) HSE Books 2013
ISBN 978 0 7176 6582 2 www.hse.gov.uk/pubns/books/l5.htm

3   *The Management of Health and Safety at Work Regulations 1999*
SI 3242/1999 The Stationery Office

4   *Reporting accidents and incidents at work: A brief guide to the Reporting of
Injuries, Diseases and Dangerous Occurrences Regulations 2013 (RIDDOR)* Leaflet
INDG453(rev1) HSE Books 2013 www.hse.gov.uk/pubns/indg453.htm

5   *The Notification of Cooling Towers and Evaporative Condensers Regulations
1992* SI 1992/2225 The Stationery Office

6   *Consulting employees on health and safety: A brief guide to the law* Leaflet
INDG232(rev2) HSE Books 2013 www.hse.gov.uk/pubns/indg232.htm

7   *Legionnaires' disease: A guide for dutyholders* Leaflet INDG458 HSE Books
2012 www.hse.gov.uk/pubns/indg458.htm

8   *Managing for health and safety* HSG65 (Third edition) HSE Books 2013
ISBN 978 0 7176 6456 6 www.hse.gov.uk/pubns/books/hsg65.htm

9   *The control of legionella: A recommended Code of Conduct for service
providers* The Legionella Control Association 2013 www.legionellacontrol.org.uk

10   *Water fittings and materials directory* Water Regulations Advisory Scheme
www.wras.co.uk/Directory

11   *Water Supply (Water Fitting) Regulations 1999* SI 1148/1999 The Stationery
Office

Further reading

BS 8580:2010 *Water quality. Risk assessments for Legionella control. Code of
practice* British Standards Institution

BS 8558:2011 *Guide to the design, installation, testing and maintenance of
services supplying water for domestic use within buildings and their curtilages*
British Standards Institution

BS EN 806 (Parts 1-5) *Specifications for installations inside buildings conveying water for human consumption* British Standards Institution

Water systems: Health Technical Memorandum 04-01: The control of Legionella, hygiene, 'safe' hot water, cold water and drinking water systems Department of Health 2006

Code of Practice: *Cooling water treatment* Water Management Society 2007 www.wmsoc.org.uk

Getting specialist help with health and safety Leaflet INDG420(rev1) HSE Books 2011 www.hse.gov.uk/pubns/indg420.htm

Minimising the risk of Legionnaires' disease TM13 The Chartered Institution of Building Services Engineers 2013

Further information

For information about health and safety, or to report inconsistencies or inaccuracies in this guidance, visit www.hse.gov.uk. You can view HSE guidance online and order priced publications from the website. HSE priced publications are also available from bookshops.

British Standards can be obtained in PDF or hard copy formats from BSI: http://shop.bsigroup.com or by contacting BSI Customer Services for hard copies only Tel: 0845 086 9001 email: cservices@bsigroup.com.

The Stationery Office publications are available from The Stationery Office, PO Box 29, Norwich NR3 1GN Tel: 0870 600 5522 Fax: 0870 600 5533 email: customer.services@tso.co.uk Website: www.tsoshop.co.uk/. They are also available from bookshops. Statutory Instruments can be viewed free of charge at www.legislation.gov.uk/ where you can also search for changes to legislation.

Printed and published by the Health and Safety Executive 11/13